THE ARTLOVER'S DAY BOOK

ALAN HUTCHISON PUBLISHING CO. LTD.

1
JANUARY

César Baldaccini, "César", (French sculptor) 1921
Chesley Bonestell (American artist) 1888
Charles François Jalabert (French painter) 1819
Bartolome Esteban Murillo (Spanish painter) 1618

3
JANUARY

August Macke (German painter) 1887
William Page (American painter) 1811
Jean Valentin (French painter) 1591

2
JANUARY

Jean-Marie Chavanne (French artist) 1797

4
JANUARY

Baron de Denon (French artist) 1747
Marsden Hartley (American painter) 1877
Augustus E. John (British artist) 1878
Edward Linley Sambourne (English artist) 1844

Breton Landscape, The Mill PAUL GAUGUIN (1848-1903)

5
JANUARY

Pompeo G. Battoni (Italian painter) 1708
Miles E. Cotman (English artist) 1810
Montague Stanley (English artist) 1809
Yves Tanguy (French painter) 1900

7
JANUARY

Claude Ferdinand Gaillard (French artist) 1834
Charles Rennie Mackintosh (British architect & artist) 1868
Patrick Nasmyth (British painter) 1787
Richard Caton Woodville (Anglo-American artist) 1856

6
JANUARY

George Thomas Doo (English engraver) 1800
Gustave Doré (French artist) 1832

8
JANUARY

Sir Lawrence Alma-Tadema (Anglo-Dutch painter) 1836
Peter Arno (American cartoonist) 1902
Serge Poliakoff (French artist) 1900
Florent J. M. Willems (Belgian painter) 1823

9
JANUARY

Adrian Paul Allinson (British artist) 1890
William-Powell Frith (English painter) 1819
Simon Vouet (French painter) 1590

11
JANUARY

A. Stirling Calder (American sculptor) 1870
Girolamo Francesco Maria Mazzola,"Il Parmigianino", (Italian
artist) 1503 Sir Bernard Partridge (English cartoonist) 1861
Jean-Baptiste van Loo (French painter) 1684

10
JANUARY

Jeffrey Jones (American artist) 1944

12
JANUARY

Georges Michel (French painter) 1765
José de Ribera (Spanish artist) 1588
John Singer Sargent (Anglo-American painter) 1856
Philip Speakman Webb (English architect) 1831

13
JANUARY

William Reid Dick (British sculptor) 1879
Charles Wellington Furse (English painter) 1868
Sulpice Guillaume Chevalier, "Paul Gavarny",
(French artist) 1804
Jan Josephzoon van Goyen (Dutch painter) 1596

14
JANUARY

Ignace-Henri-Jean-Théodore Fantin-Latour
(French painter) 1836
Berthe Morisot (French painter) 1841

15
JANUARY

Dudley Hardy (British artist) 1867
Ferdinand Georg Waldmüller (Austrian painter) 1793

16
JANUARY

William Bradley (English painter) 1801
François-Joseph Heim (French painter) 1787

Maiden with a Unicorn (95mm x 75mm)
LEONARDO DA VINCI
(1452-1519)

17
JANUARY

Eugène Carrière (French artist) 1849

18
JANUARY

Josiah Boydell (English artist) 1752
Sir Francis Grant (British painter) 1803

19
JANUARY

Alderman John Boydell (English engraver & publisher) 1719
Robert Braithwaite Martineau (English painter) 1826
Paul Cézanne (French painter) 1839

20
JANUARY

Oliver Madox Brown (English author & painter) 1821
Luca Carlevaris (Italian artist) 1665

21
JANUARY

Duncan Grant (English artist) 1885
Moritz von Schwind (German painter) 1804
Eugène E. Viollet-Le-Duc (French architect) 1814
Peter De Wint (English artist) 1784

23
JANUARY

Gilbert Ledward (English sculptor) 1888
Jan Jacob Schalch (Swiss painter) 1723
Edouard Manet (French painter) 1832

22
JANUARY

Willi Baumeister (German painter) 1889
William Brodie (British sculptor) 1815
Nicolas Lancret (French painter) 1690
Francis Picabia (French artist) 1879

24
JANUARY

Charles H.C. Baker (English artist) 1880
Robert Motherwell (American artist) 1915
Gillis van Coninxloo (Flemish painter) 1544

25
JANUARY

Marius A.J. Bauer (Dutch painter) 1864
Gouaert Flinck (German painter) 1615
Daniel Maclise (British painter) 1806

27
JANUARY

John Collier (British painter) 1850
Arthur Hughes (English artist) 1832
Josef Israels (Dutch painter) 1824
Samuel Palmer (English artist) 1805

26
JANUARY

Kees van Dongen (French painter) 1877
Benjamin Robert Haydon (British artist) 1786

28
JANUARY

Herbert Adams (American sculptor) 1858
Claes Oldenburg (American artist) 1929
Jackson Pollock (American artist) 1912
Alfred Stevens (English artist) baptised 1818

29
JANUARY

William Jacob Baer (American painter) 1860
Anne-Louis Girodet-Trioson (French artist) 1767
Sir David Murray (British artist) 1849
Sir William Rothenstein (British artist) 1872

31
JANUARY

Tilly Kettle (English painter) 1735

30
JANUARY

George Denholm Armour (British artist) 1864
Bernardo Bellotto (Italian painter) 1720
Bernardus Johannes Blommers (Dutch painter) 1845
Henry Howard (English painter) 1769

1
FEBRUARY

Jacques Émile Blanche (French painter) 1862
Thomas Cole (American painter) 1801
Albert-Charles Lebourg (French painter) 1849

3
FEBRUARY

Sir James Jebusa Shannon (Anglo-American artist) 1862
Wilhelm Trübner (German Painter) 1851

2
FEBRUARY

Oswald Achenbach (German painter) 1827
Sébastien Bourdon (French painter) 1616
George Loring Brown (American painter) 1814

4
FEBRUARY

Louis Michel Eilshemius (American painter) 1864
Myles Birket Foster (English artist) 1825
Fernand Léger (French artist) 1881
Valentine Cameron Prinsep (British artist) 1838

The Delphic Sybil MICHELANGELO BUONARROTI (1475-1564)

5
FEBRUARY

Thomas Creswick (English painter) 1811
William Nicholson (English artist) 1872

7
FEBRUARY

Henry Fuseli (British artist) 1741
Pascal A.J. Dagnan-Bouveret (French painter) 1852

6
FEBRUARY

Henry Bone (English artist) 1755
Emile Othon Friesz (French artist) 1879

8
FEBRUARY

Wilhelm Camphausen (German painter) 1818
Jean Charlot (French artist) 1898
Giovanni Francisco Barbieri "Il Guercino"
(Italian painter) 1591
Franz Marc (German painter) 1880
John Ruskin (English writer & artist) 1819

9
FEBRUARY

Richard Cotton Carline (English artist) 1896
Joseph Von Fuhrich (Austrian painter) 1800

11
FEBRUARY

Harold J.W. Gilman (English painter) 1876

10
FEBRUARY

Kasimir Malevitch (Russian painter) 1878
Ary Sheffer (French painter) 1795
Nicolas Antoine Taunay (French painter) 1755

12
FEBRUARY

Max Beckmann (German artist) 1884
Ferdinand de Braekeleer (Belgian painter) 1792
Jacques Courtois (French Painter) 1621

13
FEBRUARY

David Allan (British painter) 1744
Frank Reynolds (English artist) 1876
William Strang (British artist) 1859
Grant Wood (American painter) 1892

15
FEBRUARY

Alfred Edward Chalon (English painter) 1780
Franz Courtens (Belgian painter) 1854
Charles-François Daubigny (French artist) 1817
George Fiddes Watt (British painter) 1873

14
FEBRUARY

Maximilian Emmanuel Ainmüller (German artist) 1807
Friedrich Amerling (Austrian painter) 1803

16
FEBRUARY

Hippolyte Bellangé (French painter) 1800
Joseph Cellony (French artist) 1730
Armand Guillaumin (French painter) 1841

Procession of the Boats with Distant Smoke. Venice JOSEPH MALLORD WILLIAM TURNER (1775-1851)

17

FEBRUARY

Jan Preisler (Czechoslovakian artist) 1872

19

FEBRUARY

Luca Ferrari (French painter) 1605
Lucio Fontana (Italo-Argentinian artist) 1899

18

FEBRUARY

Thomas Girtin (English painter) 1775
John Glover (English painter) 1767
Max Klinger (German artist) 1857

20

FEBRUARY

Sir Augustus Wall Callcott (English painter) 1779
Michael von Munkacsy (Hungarian painter) 1844
Lucien Pissarro (Anglo-French painter) 1863

21
FEBRUARY

Constantin Brancusi (Romanian sculptor) 1876
Thomas Flatman (English artist) 1637
Sir William G. John (British artist) 1860
Jean-Louis-Ernest Meissonier (French artist) 1815

23
FEBRUARY

Norman A. W. Lindsay (Australian artist) 1879
George Frederick Watts (English artist) 1817

22
FEBRUARY

Eric Gill (English artist) 1882

24
FEBRUARY

Johann C. C. Dahl (Norwegian painter) 1788
Winslow Homer (American painter) 1836
Charles Lebrun (French painter) 1619
Samuel Lover (British artist) 1797

25
FEBRUARY

Pierre-Auguste Renoir (French painter) 1841

26
FEBRUARY

Honoré Daumier (French artist) 1808
Ethelbert White (English artist) 1891

27
FEBRUARY

David Jagger (English painter) 1891
Laurent de La Hyre (French painter) 1606

28
FEBRUARY

Sir John Tenniel (English artist) 1820

29

FEBRUARY

Count Balthazar Klossowski de Rola, "Balthus",
(French artist) 1908

St Jerome

LUCAS VAN LEYDEN

(1494-1533)

1

MARCH

Sir Thomas Brock (English sculptor) 1847
Oskar Kokoschka (Anglo-Austrian artist) 1886
Augustus W. N. Pugin (English architect) 1812
Augustus Saint-Gaudens (American sculptor) 1848

3

MARCH

Alexandre Decamps (French artist) 1803
Ivon Hitchens (English painter) 1893

2

MARCH

Hans Brunner (German painter) 1813
Louis Michel van Loo (French painter) 1707
Piotr Kowalski (Polish sculptor) 1927

4

MARCH

Isaac Charles Ginner (English artist) 1878
Sir Henry Raeburn (British painter) 1756

The Actress Rita Molinas FRANCISCO DE GOYA (1746-1828)

5
MARCH

Howard Pyle (American artist) 1853
Giovanni-Battista Tiepolo (Italian artist) 1696

7
MARCH

Edward Edwards (English artist) 1738
Sir Edwin Henry Landseer (English artist) 1802
Piet Mondrian (Dutch painter) 1872

6
MARCH

Charles Blair Leighton (English artist) 1823
Michelangelo Buonarroti (Italian artist) 1475

8
MARCH

George Gibbs (American artist) 1870
Percy Frederick Horton (English painter) 1897
Giovanni Batista dei Rossi (Italian painter) 1494

9
MARCH

Don Francisco Bayeu y Subias (Spanish painter) 1734
David Smith (American sculptor) 1906
Sir William Hamo Thornycroft (English sculptor) 1850

11
MARCH

Thomas Le Clear (American painter) 1818

10
MARCH

Edward Bawden (English painter) 1903
William Etty (English painter) 1787
Leonard Raven-Hill (English artist) 1867
Evan Uglow (British artist) 1932

12
MARCH

Sir William F. Douglas (British painter) 1822
Eric Henry Kennington (English artist) 1888
Benjamin Williams Leader (English painter) 1831
Stephen Catterson Smith (English painter) 1806

13
MARCH

William James Glackens (American artist) 1870
José Victoriano Gonzales, "Juan Gris", (Spanish painter) 1887
Reynolds Stone (English artist) 1909
John Zoffany (Anglo-German painter) 1733

15
MARCH

Faustin Besson (French painter) 1821
Toby Edward Rosenthal (American painter) 1848

14
MARCH

Frederick E. Church (American painter) 1826
Ferdinand Hodler (Swiss painter) 1853
Reginald Marsh (American painter) 1898
Charles Thomas Wheeler (English sculptor) 1892

16
MARCH

Guiseppe M. Crespi (Italian painter) 1665
Baron Antoine J. Gros (French painter) 1771
Robert Freebairn (English painter) 1764

The Kiss of Judas GIOTTO (1266-1336)

17
MARCH

Francesco Albani (Italian painter) 1578
François Girardon (French sculptor) 1628
John Graham (British painter) 1755
Kate Greenaway (English artist) 1846

19
MARCH

Alonso Cano (Spanish artist) 1601
Gaston Lanchaise (Franco American sculptor) 1882
Georges de La Tour (French artist) 1593
Michael Rothenstein (English artist) 1908

18
MARCH

Adam Elsheimer (German artist) 1578

20
MARCH

George Caleb Bingham (American painter) 1811
Antoine Etex (French sculptor) 1808
Jean Antoine Houdon (French sculptor) 1741
Sir Edward John Poynter (English painter) 1836

21
MARCH

James Sowerby (English illustrator) 1757
Hans Hoffmann (American painter & professor) 1880

23
MARCH

Sir Muirhead Bone (British artist) 1876
Cecil Collins (English artist) 1908
Jean Hippolyte Flandrin (French artist) 1809
Robert John Gibbings (English artist & author) 1889

22
MARCH

Randolf Caldecott (English artist) 1846
Louis Choris (Russian artist & traveller) 1795
Sir Anthony van Dyck (Anglo-Flemish painter) 1599
Ernest Lawson (American painter) 1873

24
MARCH

Philip Connard (English painter) 1875
Adrian K. G. Hill (English artist) 1895
George Lance (English painter) 1802
William Morris (English artist & poet) 1834

25
MARCH

Don Juan Carreno de Miranda (Spanish painter) 1614
John Gutzon de la Motte Borglum, "Gutzon Borglum",
(American artist) 1867

26
MARCH

William Henry Bartlett (English artist) 1809
Harry Furniss (Anglo-Irish artist) 1854
Hubert Gravelot (French artist) 1699
Julius Schnorr von Karosfeld (German painter) 1794

27
MARCH

John MacWhirter (British painter) 1839
Ludwig Miles van der Rohe (German architect) 1886
Sir William Quiller Orchardson (British painter) 1835
Edward Tennyson Reed (English caricaturist) 1860

28
MARCH

Fra Bartolommeo di Paolo (Italian painter) 1475
William Henry Hunt (English artist) 1790
William Lee-Hankey (English artist) 1869
Frederick Nash (English painter) 1782
Harry Ellis Wooldridge (English artist) 1845

29
MARCH

Edward Burra (English artist) 1905

30
MARCH

Vincent van Gogh (French painter) 1853
Francisco José de Goya y Lucientes (Spanish painter) 1746
Thomas Moore (English painter) 1790
James Ferrier Pryde (British painter) 1869

31
MARCH

Sir Oswald H. J. Birley (English painter) 1880
Antoine D. Chaudet (French sculptor) 1763
William M. Hunt (American painter) 1824
John La Farge (American painter) 1835

1

APRIL

Edwin Austin Abbey (American artist) 1852
Gaspar de Crayer (Flemish painter) 1584
William Mulready (Irish painter) 1786

3

APRIL

Charles Louis Bazin (French painter) 1802
Henry Dawson (English painter) 1811

2

APRIL

Max Ernst (French painter) 1891
Holman Hunt (English painter) 1827
John Marcellus Laroon (English painter) 1679
William Eden Nesfield (British architect) 1835

4

APRIL

Sir William Russell Flint (British artist) 1880
Grinling Gibbons (English artist) 1648
John Hoppner (English painter) 1758
Pierre Paul Prud'hon (French painter) 1758

Summer Nights WINSLOW HOMER (1836-1910)

5
APRIL

Jules Dupré (French artist) 1811
Andrew Geddes (British artist) 1783
Jean Honoré Fragonard (French painter) 1732
Marco Antonio Franceschini (Italian painter) 1648

7
APRIL

Sir Francis Legatt Chantry (English sculptor) 1781
Gérard Dou (Dutch painter) 1613
John Bernard Flannagan (American sculptor) 1895
David Low (British cartoonist) 1891

6
APRIL

Gustave Moreau (French painter) 1826
Louis Raemaekers (Dutch artist) 1869
Raffaello Sanzio Raphael (Italian painter) 1483
John Sturt (English Engraver) 1658

8
APRIL

Sir Frederick W. Burton (Irish painter) 1816
Luke Clennell (English engraver) 1781
Cornelis de Heem (Dutch painter) 1631

9
APRIL

Sir Charles Holroyd (English artist) 1861
Henri Tonks (English painter) 1862

11
APRIL

Antoine Coypel (French painter) 1661
Tristram Hillier (English painter) 1905
Jean Baptiste Isabey (French artist) 1767
John Northcote Nash (English painter) 1893

10
APRIL

Herbert Haseltine (American sculptor) 1877
Ben Nicholson (English artist) 1894
George William Russell (Irish poet & journalist
& painter) 1867

12
APRIL

Edward Bird (English painter) 1772
George Clint (English artist) 1770
Robert Delaunay (French painter) 1885
Constantin Meunier (Belgian sculptor) 1831

13
APRIL

James S. Ensor (Belgian artist) 1860
Ebenezer Landells (English Wood-Engraver) 1808
Sir Thomas Lawrence (English painter) 1769

15
APRIL

Jan van Huysum (Dutch painter) 1682
Charles Wilson Peale (American artist) 1741
Pierre E. T. Rousseau (French painter) 1812
Leonardo da Vinci (Italian artist) 1452

14
APRIL

Friedrich Amerling (Austrian painter) 1803
Robert Anning Bell (English artist) 1863

16
APRIL

William Alexander (English Artist) 1767
Thomas Hennell (English artist) 1903
Frans van Mieris, the Elder (Dutch painter) 1635

The Young Hare ALBRECHT DÜRER (1471-1528)

17
APRIL

George Vicat Cole (English artist) 1833

19
APRIL

Fernando Bottero (Columbian artist) 1932
James Heath (English engraver) 1757
Heinrich Maria von Hess (English engraver) 1798

18
APRIL

James Baylis Allen (English line engraver) 1803
Sir George Clausen (English painter) 1852
Max Webber (American painter) 1881

20
APRIL

Joan Miró (Spanish artist) 1893
Franz Xavier Winterhalter (German painter) 1806

21
APRIL

Alexander Anderson (American engraver) 1775
Ludovico Carracci (Italian artist) 1555

23
APRIL

James Sant (British artist) 1820
Joseph Mallord William Turner (English artist) 1775
Frederic Villiers (British artist & author) 1852
Antoine Vollon (French painter) 1833

22
APRIL

Evie Hone (Irish artist) 1894
Phil May (English caricaturist) 1864
Sidney Nolan (Australian painter) 1917
Odilon Redon (French artist) 1840

24
APRIL

Nathaniel Hone (Anglo-Irish painter) 1718

25
APRIL

Gustave Boulanger (French painter) 1824
Richard Boyle Earl of Burlington
(English amateur architect) 1695
Bridget Riley (English artist) 1931

27
APRIL

Samuel Finley Breese Morse
(American painter & inventor) 1791

26
APRIL

John James Audubon (American naturalist & artist) 1785
Harry Bates (English sculptor) 1850
Eugène Delacroix (French painter) 1798
Edmund Charles Tarbell (American painter) 1862

28
APRIL

Cecil Charles Windsor Aldin (English artist) 1870
Frances Hodgkins (Anglo-Australian painter) 1870
Philip Alexius Laszlo de Lombos (English painter) 1869
Arthur Watts (British artist) 1883

29
APRIL

Frank Auerbach (Anglo-German painter) 1931
David Cox (English painter) 1783
John William Inchbold (British painter) 1830
Gian Antonio Pellegrini (Italian artist) 1675

30
APRIL

Jacques Louis David (French painter) 1748
Franz von Defregger (Austrian painter) 1835
Jean François Portaels (Belgian artist) 1818
Léon Adolphe Willette (French artist) 1857

A Lady Standing
HUBERT GRAVELOT (1699-1773)

1
MAY

Jules Adolphe Aimé Breton (French painter) 1827
John Westbrooke Chandler (English painter) 1764
George Inness (American painter) 1825
Frederick Sandys (English artist) 1832

3
MAY

Philip Hermogenes Calderon (British painter) 1833

2
MAY

Augustus Leopold Egg (English artist) 1816
Nicholas Pocock (English artist) 1741

4
MAY

Joseph Farquharson (British painter) 1846
Baron Francois P.S. Gérard (French painter) 1770
Sir Thomas Lawrence (English painter) 1769

The Rocks of Belle-Isle CLAUDE MONET (1840-1926)

5
MAY

Henry Bernard Chalon (English painter) 1771

7
MAY

Richard Norman Shaw (British architect) 1831

6
MAY

Frank Bramley (English artist) 1857
Ernest Ludwig Kirchner (German painter) 1880

8
MAY

Alphonse Legros (Anglo-French artist) 1837

9
MAY

Howard Carter (English archaeologist & artist) 1874
Samuel Cousins (English engraver) 1801
Randolf Schwabe (English Landscape artist) 1885
Anton Alexander von Werner (German painter) 1843

11
MAY

Richard Ansdell (English painter) 1815
Jean Baptiste Carpeaux (French sculptor) 1827
Salvador Dali (Spanish artist) 1904
Paul Nash (English artist) 1889

10
MAY

Luigi Bisi (Italian painter) 1814
Bernard Finegan Gribble (English artist) 1872

12
MAY

Edward Lear (English author & artist) 1812
Anto Raphael Mengs (German painter) 1728
Dante Gabriel Rossetti (English artist & poet) 1828
Frank Stella (American painter) 1936

13
MAY

Sir Frank Brangwyn (British artist) 1867
Georges Braque (French artist) 1882
Baron Pierre N. Guérin (French painter) 1774
Léopold Robert (French painter) 1794

15
MAY

Claud Lovat Fraser (British artist) 1890
Jasper Johns (American artist) 1930
Carlo Maratta (Italian painter) 1625
Alfred Rethel (German painter) 1816

14
MAY

Thomas Gainsborough (English painter) 1727

16
MAY

John Sell Cotman (British painter) 1782
James Lonsdale (English painter) 1777

The Marriage of the Virgin

RAPHAEL (1483-1520)

17
MAY

Raymond Bigot (French artist) 1872

18
MAY

Sir Nathaniel Dance-Holland (English painter) 1735
Walter A. Gropius (German architect) 1883

19
MAY

Antoine Béranger (French painter) 1785
Sir Oswald Walters Brierly (English painter) 1817
Barnett Freedman (English painter) 1901
Jacob Jordaens (Flemish painter) 1593

20
MAY

Francis Cotes (English painter) 1726
Henri-Edmond Cross (French painter) 1856
Thomas Webster (English painter) 1800

21
MAY

Alan Hervey D'Egville (English artist) 1891
Alexander Pope (English poet & artist) 1688
Henri Rousseau, "Douanier", (French painter) 1844

23
MAY

Chester Beach (American sculptor) 1881
Bertholet Flemal (Flemish painter) 1614
Antoine Pesne (French painter) 1683
James Pradier (Swiss sculptor) 1792

22
MAY

Mary Cassatt (American artist) 1845
Sir Aston Webb (English architect) 1849

24
MAY

Albrecht Dürer (German artist) 1471
Charles Napier Hemy (English painter) 1841
Frederick Walker (English painter) 1840
Sir Ernest Albert Waterlow (English painter) 1850

25
MAY

Boris Artzybasheff (Russian/American artist) 1899
Mather Brown (Anglo-American painter) 1761
Jean Charles Cazin (painter) 1841
Edward Morland Lewis (British artist) 1903

27
MAY

Nicolas Grigorescu (Romanian painter) 1838
Georges Rouault (French artist) 1871

26
MAY

Frederick Barnard (British illustrator) 1846
Philippe de Champaigne (French painter) 1602
Carlo Dolci (Italian painter) 1616
Sir Hubert von Herkomer (British artist) 1849

28
MAY

Alexander Calame (Swiss painter) 1810
Hans Makart (Austrian painter) 1840

Embarcation for Cythera JEAN-ANTOINE WATTEAU (1684-1721)

29
MAY

Eugene Meeks (American painter) 1843

30
MAY

Clemens Bewer (German painter) 1820

31
MAY

Jules Chéret (French artist) 1836
Alphonse Marie de Neuville (French artist) 1836
William Heath Robinson (English artist) 1872
Walter Richard Sickert (English artist) 1860

The Card Players PAUL CÉZANNE (1839-1906)

1
JUNE

Louis Eugène Charpentier (French painter) 1811
Hugh Thompson (British artist) 1860

2
JUNE

Paul Albert Besnard (French painter) 1849

3
JUNE

Raoul Dufy (French artist) 1877
William Hilton (English artist) 1786
Johan Barthold Jongkind (Dutch artist) 1819
Sir William Charles Ross (English artist) 1794

4
JUNE

John Le Keux (English engraver) 1783
Edward Prior (English architect) 1852

The Bridge at Nantes JEAN-BAPTISTE COROT (1796-1875)

5
JUNE

Henri Bonaventure Monnier (French artist) 1805
Marco Ricci (Italian painter) 1676
William Patrick Roberts (English artist) 1895

7
JUNE

Samuel John Lamorna Birch (English painter) 1869
Paul Gauguin (French artist) 1848

6
JUNE

Anna Airy (British painter) 1882
Charles Joshua Chaplin (French painter) 1825
John Trumbull (American painter) 1756
Diego Rodriguez de Silva y Vélasquez (Spanish painter) 1599

8
JUNE

Thomas Faed (British painter) 1826
John Everett Millais (British artist) 1829
Thomas Rickman (English architect) 1776

9
JUNE

Edouard Goerg (Franco-Austrian artist) 1891
John Rattenbury Skeaping (English sculptor) 1901
Dame Ethel Walker (English artist) 1861

11
JUNE

John Constable (English painter) 1776
William Nelson Gardiner (Irish engraver & bookseller) 1766

10
JUNE

Jean J. B. Constant (French painter) 1845
Gustave Courbet (French painter) 1819
Sir James Guthrie (British painter) 1859

12
JUNE

Frederick James Porter (British artist) 1883
Henry Scott Tuke (English painter) 1858

13
JUNE

Joseph Highmore (English painter) 1692

14
JUNE

Herbert Dicksee (English artist) 1862
Louis Dorigny (French artist) 1654
Charles William Sherborn (English engraver) 1831

15
JUNE

Hablot Knight Browne, "Phiz", (English artist) 1815
Malvina Hoffmann (American sculptor) 1887

16
JUNE

Sir George James Frampton (English artist) 1860
John Linnell (English artist) 1792

Lovers with a Cat OSKAR KOKOSCHKA (1886-1980)

17
JUNE

André Derain (French painter) 1880

18
JUNE

Henry Hugh Armstead (English sculptor) 1828
Allart van Everdingen (Dutch artist) 1621

19
JUNE

Jean-Baptiste Monnoyer (French painter) 1636
Raphael Sanzio Morghen (Italian engraver) 1758
Sir Frank Short (English artist) 1857

20
JUNE

(Joseph-Florentin-) Léon Bonnat (French painter) 1833
Salvator Rosa (Italian artist) 1615
George Edmund Street (English architect) 1824

21
JUNE

Daniel Carter Beard (American illustrator & author) 1850
Henry Taylor Lamb (English painter) 1883
Henry Ossawa Tanner (American painter) 1859

23
JUNE

Philipp Otto Runge (German artist & poet) 1777

22
JUNE

Pavel Andreyevich Fedotov (Russian painter) 1815
Gwendolen Mary John, "Gwen John", (English painter) 1876
Rupert Lee (English sculptor) 1887

24
JUNE

Ferdinand Bol (Dutch painter) 1616
Rex John Whistler (British artist) 1905

25
JUNE

Robert Henri (American painter) 1865
Sam Francis (American painter) 1923

27
JUNE

François Biard (French painter) 1801

26
JUNE

George Morland (English painter) 1763
Jean-Baptiste Pigalle (French sculptor) 1714

28
JUNE

Sir David Young Cameron (British artist) 1865
William John Muller (British painter) 1812

29
JUNE

Ann Mary Newton (English painter) 1832
Peter Paul Rubens (Flemish artist) 1577
John Quincy Adams Ward (American sculptor) 1830

30
JUNE

Sir Stanley Spencer (English painter) 1891
Horace Vernet (French painter) 1789

Englishwoman in Contemporary Dress
HANS HOLBEIN
(1497-1543)

1
JULY

Jean Lurçat (French artist) 1892

3
JULY

John Singleton Copley (American painter) 1738
Erskine Nicol (British painter) 1825
Johann Friedrich Overbeck (German painter) 1789

2
JULY

George Dunlop Leslie (English painter) 1835
Sir Lawrence Weaver (English architect) 1876

4
JULY

John Lucas (English painter) 1807
William Lodge (English artist) 1649
Samuel William Reynolds (English artist) 1773
Marcus C. Stone (English artist) 1840

The Serving Maids DIEGO VELAZQUEZ (1599-1660)

5
JULY

Louis Léopold Boilly (French painter) 1761
Paris Bordone (Italian painter) 1500
Jean Cocteau (French artist) 1889
André Lhote (French painter & writer) 1885

6
JULY

John Flaxman (English artist) 1755
George Percy Jacomb-Hood (English artist) 1857
André Dunoyer de Segonzac (French artist) 1884

7
JULY

Marc Chagall (Russian artist) 1887
Félicien Rops (Belgian artist) 1833

8
JULY

Kathe Kollwitz (German artist) 1867
Jacques-Philippe Lebas (French engraver) 1707
John Newman (English architect & antiquary) 1786

9
JULY

David Hockney (British artist) 1937

11
JULY

Henry Mathew Brock (English artist) 1875
Charles-Antoine Coypel (French painter) 1694
Roger de La Fresnaye (French painter) 1885
Giovanni Battista Salvi, "Sassoferato", (Italian painter) 1605

10
JULY

Benjamin Paul Akers (American sculptor) 1825
Bernard Buffet (French artist) 1928
Giorgio de Chirico (Italian artist) 1888
Camille Pissarro (French painter) 1831
James Abbott McNeil Whistler (American artist) 1834

12
JULY

Eugène Louis Boudin (French painter) 1824
Hugh Ferriss (American architect & artist) 1889
Edwin Longsden Long (English painter) 1829
Amadeo Modigliani (Italian artist) 1884

13
JULY

Wenceslaus Hollar (Bohemian engraver) 1607

14
JULY

Gustav Eberlein (German sculptor) 1847
Gustav Klimt (Austrian artist) 1862
John Frederick Lewis (English painter) 1805
Sir Robert Strange (British engraver) 1771

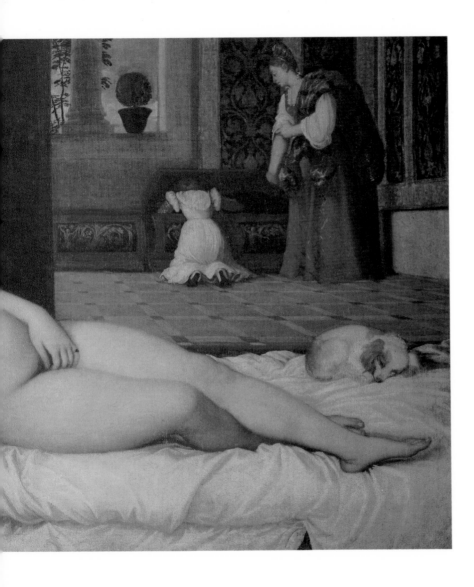

Venus of Urbino
TITIAN
(1477/89 – 1576)

15
JULY

Reinhold Begas (German artist) 1831
Sir Henry Cole (English artist & writer) 1808
Inigo Jones (English architect & scenographer) 1573
Rembrandt Harmensz van Rijn, "Rembrandt"
(Dutch artist) 1606

17
JULY

Hippolyte Delaroche (French painter) 1797
Lyonel Feininger (American painter) 1871
Tom Webster (English cartoonist) 1890

16
JULY

Jean-Baptiste Camille Corot (French painter) 1796
Sir Josuah Reynolds (English painter) 1723

18
JULY

Paul Dubois (French sculptor) 1829
Hyacinthe Rigaud (French painter) 1659

19
JULY

Edgar Degas (French artist) 1834
John Martin (English painter) 1789
Alfred Waterhouse (English architect) 1830

21
JULY

Louis Corinth (German painter) 1858
Albert Gustaf Aristide Edelfelt (Finnish painter) 1854
Sir John Gilbert (English artist) 1817
William Borthwick Johnstone (British painter) 1804

20
JULY

Max Liebermann (German artist) 1847

22
JULY

Edward Hooper (American artist) 1882
Eric Ravilious (English artist) 1903

23
JULY

Herman Corrodi (Italian painter) 1844

24
JULY

Eugen Blaas (Italian painter) 1843

25
JULY

Thomas Eakins (American painter) 1844
Sir James Thornhill (English painter) 1675

26
JULY

Jankel Adler (Polish painter) 1895
George Catlin (American painter & traveller) 1796
George Grosz (German artist) 1893
Ignacio Zuloaga (Spanish painter) 1870

Marriage à la Mode: The Countess's Morning Levée WILLIAM HOGARTH (1697-1764)

27
JULY

Edward Onslow Ford (English sculptor) 1852

28
JULY

Marcel Duchamp (French artist) 1887

29
JULY

Peter von Hess (German painter) 1792
Eastman Johnson (American painter) 1824

30
JULY

Henry Moore (English sculptor) 1898
Giorgio Vasari (Italian architect, artist & writer) 1511

31
JULY

Jean Philippe Arthur Dubuffet (French artist) 1901

Self-Portrait
SAMUEL PALMER
(1805-1881)

1
AUGUST

Edward Penny (English painter) 1714
Sebastiano Ricci (Italian painter) 1659
Richard Wilson (British painter) 1714

3
AUGUST

James Wyatt (English architect) 1746

2
AUGUST

Gérard Audran (French engraver) 1640
Arthur Garfield Dove (American painter) 1880
Samuel Dirksz van Hoogstraten (Dutch painter) 1627
Pierre Charles L'Enfant (French architect) 1754

4
AUGUST

Gilbert Spencer (English painter) 1892

The Ballet Class EDGAR DEGAS (1834-1917)

5
AUGUST

Louis William Wain (English artist) 1860

7
AUGUST

Emil Nolde (German painter) 1867

6
AUGUST

John Frederick Thomas Jane (British artist) 1865

8
AUGUST

George Cattermole (English painter) 1800
Sir Geodfrey Kneller (Anglo-German painter) 1646

9
AUGUST

Sir John William Simpson (English architect) 1858
Mahonri Mackintosh Young (American sculptor) 1877

10
AUGUST

Arthur Williams Devis (English painter) 1762
William Michael Harnett (American artist) 1848
Charles Samuel Keene (English artist) 1823
Leonard Knyff (Dutch painter) 1650

11
AUGUST

Joseph Nollekens (English sculptor) 1737

12
AUGUST

Thomas Bewick (English wood-engraver) 1753
Sir Alfred Gilbert (English sculptor) 1854
Arthur Ambrose McEvoy (British painter) 1878
Abbott Handerson Thayers (American painter) 1849

13
AUGUST

C. R. W. Nevinson (English artist) 1889

15
AUGUST

Agostino Carracci (Italian painter) 1557
Walter Crane (English artist) 1845
Eugène Napoléon Flandrin (French painter) 1809
Alexander Runciman (British painter) 1736

14
AUGUST

Briton Riviere (British painter) 1840
Charles Horace Vernet, "Carle", (French painter) 1758
Claude-Joseph Vernet (French painter) 1714

16
AUGUST

Carl-Frederik van Breda (Swedish painter) 1759
Andrea del Sarto (Italian painter) 1486

The Morning Walk
THOMAS GAINSBOROUGH
(1727-1788)

17
AUGUST

Thomas Stothard (English artist) 1755
John Varley (English artist & writer) 1778

19
AUGUST

Gebrand van den Eeckhout (Dutch painter) 1621

18
AUGUST

Giacomo Balla (Italian painter) 1871
David Lucas (English engraver) 1802

20
AUGUST

Narcisse-Virgile Diaz de la Pēna (French painter) 1808

21

AUGUST

Aubrey Vincent Beardsley (English artist) 1872
Jean-Baptiste Greuze (French painter) 1725

22

AUGUST

Jean-Charles Frontier (French painter) 1701

A Ruined House
JOHN SELL COTMAN
(1782-1842)

23
AUGUST

Baron Egide C. G. Wappers (Belgian painter) 1803

24
AUGUST

Sir Henry Maximilian Beerbohm (English cartoonist) 1872
Léon Cogniet (French artist) 1794
George Stubbs (English painter) 1724

25
AUGUST

Alfred Henri Robinson Thornton (English painter) 1863
Louis Etienne Watelet (French painter) 1782

26
AUGUST

Cowan Dobson (English painter) 1893
José Villegas (Spanish painter) 1848

27
AUGUST

Sydney Lee (English artist) 1866

28
AUGUST

Sir Edward Burne-Jones (English artist) 1833
Alfred Chew Leete (English artist) 1882
Jacob Thompson (English painter) 1806
Constant Toyon (French painter) 1810

29
AUGUST

Jean-Auguste-Dominique Ingres (French painter) 1780
John Leech (English artist) 1817
Sir John Sulman (Australian architect) 1849
Jack Yeats (Irish painter) 1871

30
AUGUST

Jacques-Louis David (French painter) 1748

31
AUGUST

William Wilkins (English architect) 1778

Landscape with
Psyche outside
the Palace
of Cupid
(The Enchanted Castle)
CLAUDE (Lorrain)
(1600-1682)

1

SEPTEMBER

Gustave Ricard (French painter) 1843

2

SEPTEMBER

Louis Chéron (French artist) 1660

3

SEPTEMBER

Jules Ferdinand Jacquemart (French artist) 1837
Thomas Goff Lupton (English engraver) 1791
Joseph Wright (English painter) 1734

4

SEPTEMBER

Albert Joseph Moore (English painter) 1841

Nana
EDOUARD MANET
(1832-1883)

5
SEPTEMBER

Kaspar David Friedrich (German artist) 1774
Maurice-Quentin de Latour (French painter) 1704

7
SEPTEMBER

Edward Francis Burney (English painter) 1760
Jean Alexandre Joseph Falguière (French sculptor) 1831

6
SEPTEMBER

Percy Hutton Fearon (British cartoonist) 1874

8
SEPTEMBER

William Collins (English painter) 1788
Abraham Cooper (English painter) 1787
Ozias Humphry (English painter) 1742

9
SEPTEMBER

Eduard Hildebrandt (German painter) 1818
Alexander Nasmyth (British painter) 1758
Charles Pears (British artist) 1873
James Smetham (English artist & essayist) 1821

11
SEPTEMBER

Nikola Abraham Abildgaard (Danish painter) 1743

10
SEPTEMBER

Guillaume Geefs (Belgian sculptor) 1806
Sir John Soane (British architect) 1753

12
SEPTEMBER

Anselm Feuerbach (German painter) 1829
Fernand Khnopff (Belgian artist) 1858
Ben Shan (Russian/American painter) 1898
William Bell Scott (British poet & painter) 1811

13
SEPTEMBER

Jan Brueghel, the Younger (Flemish painter) 1601
Jean Ignace Isidore Gérard, "Grandville",
(French caricaturist) 1803
Joseph Stannard (English painter) 1797

15
SEPTEMBER

Ernest Crofts (English Painter) 1847
Frank Lewis Emanuel (English artist) 1865
Solomon Joseph Solomon (English artist) 1860

14
SEPTEMBER

Charles Dana Gibson (American artist) 1867
Sir Peter Lely (Anglo-Dutch painter) 1618

16
SEPTEMBER

Hans Arp (French artist) 1887
Jacopo Robusti Tintoretto (Italian painter) 1518

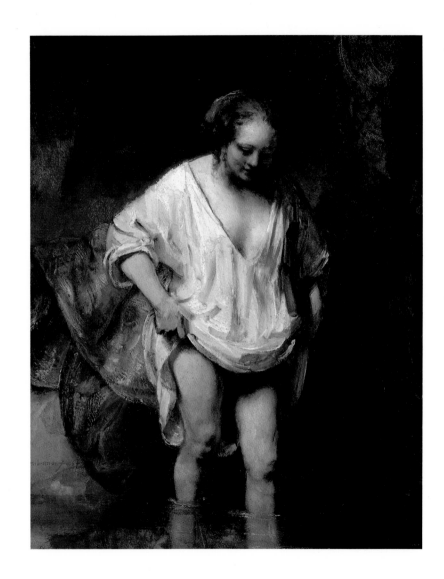

A Woman Bathing
in a Stream
REMBRANDT HARMENSZ.
VAN RIJN.
(1606-1669)

17
SEPTEMBER

Charles-Joseph Beauverie (French artist) 1839
Frederick Goodall (British artist) 1822

18
SEPTEMBER

Richard Doyle (English artist) 1824
Lady Sybil Grant (English writer & artist) 1879
Anton Mauve (Dutch painter) 1838
Sir John Steell (English sculptor) 1804

19
SEPTEMBER

George Frederick Arthur Belcher (British artist) 1875
William Dyce (British painter) 1806

20
SEPTEMBER

Edward Calvert (English artist) 1799
Théodore Chassériau (French painter) 1819
Gilbert Stuart Newton (British artist) 1794

21
SEPTEMBER

Francesco Bartolozzi (Italian engraver) 1728
Denis Echeverry (French painter) 1867
Walter William Ouless (British painter) 1728

23
SEPTEMBER

Peter von Cornelius (German painter) 1783
Frantisek Kupta (Czech painter) 1871
Suzanne Valadon (French artist) 1867

22
SEPTEMBER

Jean Baptiste Auguste Clesinger (French sculptor) 1814
Matthew Merian (Swiss engraver) 1593

24
SEPTEMBER

Antoine Louis Barye (French artist) 1796
Henry Raeburn Macbeth-Raeburn (British engraver) 1860

25
SEPTEMBER

Arthur Hacker (English painter) 1858
Mark Rothko (American artist) 1903

27
SEPTEMBER

Maurice Frederick Codner (English painter) 1888
George Cruikshank (English artist) 1792
Thomas Nast (American caricaturist) 1840
Nicolas Constantinovich Roerich (Russian painter) 1874

26
SEPTEMBER

Thomas Sidney Cooper (English painter) 1803
Arthur Bowen Davies (American painter) 1862
Jean Louis André Théodore Géricault (French painter) 1791
Thomas Jones (British painter) 1742

28
SEPTEMBER

Charles Bell Birch (English sculptor) 1832
George De Forest Brush (American painter) 1855
Alexandre Cabanel (French painter) 1823
Michelangelo Merisi da Caravaggio (Italian painter) 1573

29
SEPTEMBER

François Boucher (French painter) 1703
Charles Antoine Coysevox (French sculptor) 1640
Michael Dahl (Swedish painter) 1656

30
SEPTEMBER

Karle Begas (German artist) 1794
Robert Walker Macbeth (British artist) 1848
Jehan George Vibert (French painter) 1840

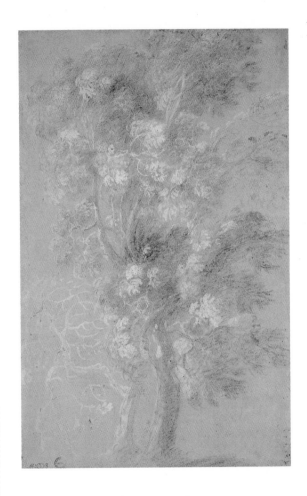

Trees in a Gale
CLAUDE LORRAIN
(1600-1682)

1
OCTOBER

José Benlliure y Gil (Spanish painter) 1855
Karl Theodor von Piloty (German painter) 1826
Sir Robert Smirke (English architect) 1781
Giacomo Barozzio da Vignola (Italian architect) 1507

3
OCTOBER

Pierre Bonnard (French artist) 1867
Pieter Casteels (Flemish painter) 1684
Albert Houthuesen (Anglo-Dutch artist) 1903
Stanislas Victor Edmond Lépine (French painter) 1835

2
OCTOBER

Johann Konrad Gessner (Swiss painter) 1764
Allan Ramsay (British painter) 1713
Charles Ricketts (British painter) 1866

4
OCTOBER

Lucas Cranach, the elder (German artist) 1472
Henri Gaudier-Brezeska (French sculptor) 1891
Jean François Millet (French artist) 1814

The Marriage of
Giovanni Arnolfini
and Giovanna Cerami
JAN VAN EYCK
(act. 1422 – d. 1441)

5

OCTOBER

Jean Baptiste Edouard Detaille (French artist) 1848
Francesco Guardi (Italian painter) 1712
Ludwig Knaus (German painter) 1829
Glyn Warren Philpot (English painter) 1884

7

OCTOBER

John White Alexander (American painter) 1856
Harrington Mann (British artist) 1864

6

OCTOBER

James Basire (English engraver) 1730
Le Corbusier (French architect) 1887
Einar Nerman (Swedish artist) 1888

8

OCTOBER

Joseph Anton Adolph (English painter) 1729
Pierre Falconet (French painter) 1741
Sir Alfred James Munnings (British painter) 1878

9
OCTOBER

Wilfrid de Glehn (English artist) 1870

11
OCTOBER

James Barry (Irish painter) 1741
Charles Robert Leslie (Anglo-American painter) 1794

10
OCTOBER

Alberto Giacometti (Swiss artist) 1901
Nicolas de Largillierre (French painter) 1656
Jean-Antoine Watteau (French painter) 1684
Benjamin West (American painter) 1738

12
OCTOBER

David Scott (British painter) 1806
William Westall (English painter) 1781

13
OCTOBER

Mariotto Albertinelli (Italian painter) 1474
Hermann Wilhelm Bissen (Danish sculptor) 1798
Sir James Thomas Knowles (English architect) 1831

15
OCTOBER

Johann Heinrich von Dannecker (German sculptor) 1758
Wilhelm von Kaulbach (German painter) 1804
James Joseph Jacques Tissot (French painter) 1836

14
OCTOBER

Alessio Baldovinetti (Italian painter) 1427
Pieter van der Faes, "Sir Pieter", (English painter) 1618
Cornelius Janssen (or Johnson) (Dutch painter) 1593
Adolphe Joseph Thomas Monticelli (French painter) 1824

16
OCTOBER

Arnold Böcklin (Swiss-German painter) 1827
Russell Cheney (American painter) 1881
Daniel Nicholas Chodowiecki (Polish artist) 1726
Frank Cadogan Cowper (English artist) 1877
Valentine Green (English engraver) 1739

An Autumn Landscape with a View of Het Steen in the Early Morning PETER PAUL RUBENS (1577-1640)

17
OCTOBER

Pierre Antoine Baudoin (French painter) 1723
Adolphe Flex Cals (French painter) 1810

19
OCTOBER

Charles Robert Leslie (English painter) 1794
Henry Singleton (English artist) 1766

18
OCTOBER

Giovanni Antonio Canaletto (Italian Painter) 1697
Sir Luke Fildes (British Painter) 1844
Thomas Phillips (English Portrait Painter) 1770

20
OCTOBER

Gerard Edelinck (Flemish engraver) 1640
Henry Inman (American painter) 1801
Sir Christopher Wren (British architect) 1632

21
OCTOBER

Richard Cromwell Carpenter (English architect) 1812
Domenico Zampieri, "Domenichino", (Italian painter) 1581

22
OCTOBER

James Kay (British painter) 1858
James Northcote (English painter) 1746
Robert Rauschenberg (American artist) 1925
Sir Matthew Arnold Bracy Smith (English painter) 1879

Study of a Woman
THOMAS GAINSBOROUGH
(1727-1788)

23

OCTOBER

Jean-Louis Forain (French artist) 1852
Wilhelm Leibi (German painter) 1844
John James Masquerier (English painter) 1778
James Ward (English artist) 1769

24

OCTOBER

William Aikman (British painter) 1682
Charles Conder (English artist) 1868
Jan Lievens (Dutch painter) 1607
John Sartain (Anglo-American engraver) 1808

The Third Duke
of Richmond
with the
Charlton Hunt
GEORGE STUBBS
(1724-1806)

25
OCTOBER

Richard-Parkes Bonington (English artist) 1802
Arshile Gorky (American painter) 1904
Pablo Ruiz Picasso (Franco-Spanish artist) 1881
Claude Allin Shepperson (English artist) 1867

27
OCTOBER

Peter Blume (American painter) 1906
William Newton (English architect) 1735
Joseph Strutt (English artist) 1749

26
OCTOBER

Vasili Vereschchagin (Russian painter) 1842
Sir Nevile Rodwell Wilkinson (English artist) 1869

28
OCTOBER

Francis Bacon (British artist) 1909
William Hodges (English artist) 1744
Homer Dodge Martin (American painter) 1836

29
OCTOBER

Edward Wadsworth (English painter) 1889

31
OCTOBER

Philippe Jacques de Loutherbourg (French painter) 1740
Pierre Puget (French sculptor) 1622
Sir George Reid (British painter) 1841
Johannes Vermeer (Dutch painter) 1632

30
OCTOBER

Sawrey Gilpin (English painter) 1733
Angelica Kauffmann (Anglo-Swiss painter) 1741
Antonin Mercié (French sculptor) 1845
Alfred Sisley (French artist) 1899

1
NOVEMBER

Jules Bastien-Lepage (French painter) 1848
Antonio Canova (Italian sculptor) 1757
Pietro da Cortona (Italian painter & architect) 1596
L. S. Lowry (English painter) 1887

3
NOVEMBER

Annibale Carracci (Italian painter) 1560
Benvenuto Cellini (Italian artist) 1500

2
NOVEMBER

Jean-Baptiste-Siméon Chardin (French painter) 1699
Sir Arthur Stockdale Cope (English painter) 1857
James Henry Haseltine (American artist) 1833

4
NOVEMBER

Gerrit van Honthorst (Dutch painter) 1590
Sir Robert Stodart Lorimer (British architect) 1864
Guido Reni (Italian painter) 1575

Spring PIETER BRUEGHEL THE YOUNGER (c. 1564-1638)

5

NOVEMBER

Washington Allston (American painter) 1779
Philip De Koninck (Dutch painter) 1619
Thomas Sully (American painter) 1783

7

NOVEMBER

Paul Jacques-Aimé Baudry (French painter) 1828
Antoine Chazal (French artist) 1793
William Hole (British artist) 1846
Francisco de Zurbarán (Spanish painter) 1598

6

NOVEMBER

Louis René Moilliet (Swiss painter) 1880

8

NOVEMBER

David Farquharson (British painter) 1840

The Cornfield
JOHN CONSTABLE
(1776-1837)

9
NOVEMBER

Sir George Howland Beaumont (English painter) 1753
Sir Giles Gilbert Scott (British architect) 1880

11
NOVEMBER

Sir Charles John Holmes (English painter) 1868
Paul Signac (French painter) 1863
Jean Edouard Vuillard (French painter) 1868

10
NOVEMBER

Jacob Epstein (Anglo-American sculptor) 1880
William Hogarth (British artist) 1697
Adrian van de Velde (Dutch artist) 1630

12
NOVEMBER

Bartolommeo Bandinelli (Italian sculptor) 1493
Auguste Rodin (French sculptor) 1840

13
NOVEMBER

Robert Scott (English engraver) 1777
John Byam Lister Shaw (English artist) 1872

15
NOVEMBER

Jean Louis Bezard (French painter) 1799
Georgia O'Keefe (American painter) 1887

14
NOVEMBER

John Armstrong (English painter) 1893
Elisabeth Frink (English sculptor) 1930
Claude Monet (French painter) 1840
Francis Nicholson (English painter) 1753

16
NOVEMBER

Francis Danby (Irish painter) 1793
Louise Jopling (English artist) 1843
William Friend De Morgan (English artist & novelist) 1839

17
NOVEMBER

Agnolo di Cosimo, "Il Bronzino", (Italian painter & poet) 1503
Noel Nicolas Coypel (French painter) 1690
Sir Charles Lock Eastlake (English artist)
François Louis Français (French painter) 1814

19
NOVEMBER

Eustache Le Sueur (French painter) baptised 1617
John Hungerford Pollen (English artist & author) 1820
Johannes Stark (English artist) 1794
Bertel Thorwaldsen (Danish sculptor) 1770

18
NOVEMBER

Gaspar de Crayer (Flemish artist) 1582
Frank Owen Dobson (English sculptor) 1886
Stanhope Alexander Forbes (British artist) 1857
Wyndham Lewis (English painter & author) 1884

20
NOVEMBER

Guy François, "le grand François", (French painter) 1580
Paul Potter (Dutch artist) 1625

Eleonora da Toledo
with her son Giovanni
AGNOLO BRONZINO
(1503-1572)

21
NOVEMBER

James Clarke Hook (English painter) 1819
René Magritte (Belgian artist) 1898
Francis Stevens (English painter) 1781
Cornelius Varley (English painter) 1781

23
NOVEMBER

José Clemente Orozco (Mexican artist) 1883

22
NOVEMBER

Johan Bull (Norwegian artist) 1893
Cyrus Edwin Dallin (American sculptor) 1861
Anthony-Vandyke Copley Fielding (English painter) 1787
William Leighton Leitch (British painter) 1804

24
NOVEMBER

John Bacon (English sculptor) 1740
Charles Meryon (French etcher) 1821
Henri de Toulouse- Lautrec -Monfa (French artist) 1864
Norman Wilkinson (English artist) 1878

25
NOVEMBER

Maurice Denis (French artist & writer) 1870

27
NOVEMBER

Hercules Brabazon (English painter) 1821
Paul Jean Clays (Belgian painter) 1819
Sir Francis Bernard Dicksee (English artist) 1853
Tsugouharu Fougita (Japanese artist) 1886

26
NOVEMBER

William Sidney Mount (American painter) 1807

28
NOVEMBER

William Blake (English artist & poet) 1757

29
NOVEMBER

Sir William Blake Richmond (English artist) 1842
George Loraine Stampa (British artist) 1875
Emile Charles Marie Wavters (Belgian painter) 1846

30
NOVEMBER

Adolphe William Bouguereau (French painter) 1825
Andrea Palladio (Italian architect) 1508

View of Delft
JAN VERMEER
(1632-1675)

1

DECEMBER

George Daziel (English wood-engraver) 1815

3

DECEMBER

Eduard Bedemann (German painter) 1811
Cecil Gordon Lawson (English painter) 1851
Lord Frederic Leighton (English artist) 1830
Victor Pasmore (English artist) 1908

2

DECEMBER

Sir Francis Carruthers Gould (English cartoonist) 1844
Alfred William Parsons (English artist) 1847
Georges Seurat (French painter) 1859

4

DECEMBER

George Henry Boughton (English painter) 1833
Wassily Kandinsky (Russian artist) 1866

The Lute Player MICHELANGELO MERISI DA CARAVAGGIO (1571-1610)

5
DECEMBER

David Garshen Bomberg (British artist) 1890
Alfred Manessier (French painter) 1911

7
DECEMBER

Gian Lorenzo Bernini (Italian artist) 1598
Stuart Davis (British artist) 1894
William James Linton (English engraver) 1812

6
DECEMBER

Jean-Frédéric Bazille (French painter) 1841

8
DECEMBER

Gonzales Conques (Flemish painter) 1614
Lucien Freud (English painter) 1922
Aristide Maillol (French sculptor) 1861
Adolf Friedrich Erdman von Menzel (German artist) 1815

9
DECEMBER

Mark Gertler (British painter) 1891
Friedrich August Moritz Retzsch (German artist) 1779

11
DECEMBER

John Acton Adams (English artist) 1836
René Bull (British artist) 1872
Pieter Codde (Dutch painter) 1599

10
DECEMBER

Ernest Shepard (English artist) 1879
Adriaen van Ostade (Dutch artist) 1610

12
DECEMBER

Sir William Beechey (English painter) 1753
Jules Eugène Lenepveu (French painter) 1819
Eduard Munch (Norwegian painter) 1863
Leonard Cambell Taylor (English painter) 1874

13
DECEMBER

Franz Lenbach (German painter) 1836
John Piper (English artist) 1903
Diego Rivera (Mexican artist) 1886

15
DECEMBER

Sir Alfred East (English artist) 1849
Martin Hardie (English artist & museum official) 1875
George Romney (English painter) 1734
David Teniers, the younger (Flemish painter) 1610

14
DECEMBER

François Hubert Drouais (French painter) 1727
Roger Elliot Fry (English painter & writer) 1866
Pierre-Cécile Puvis de Chavannes (French painter) 1824

16
DECEMBER

Sir George Scharf (British artist) 1820

17
DECEMBER

François Marius Granet (French painter) 1775
Sir George Hayter (English painter) 1792
Paul César Helleu (French artist) 1859
Joseph Nash (English artist) 1809

18
DECEMBER

David Adolf Constant Artz (Dutch painter) 1837
Ludolf Backhuysen (Dutch painter) 1631
Paul Klee (Swiss-German painter) 1879
Frank O. Salisbury (British painter) 1874

19
DECEMBER

Baron Auguste G. L. B. Desnoyers (French engraver) 1779

20
DECEMBER

Nicolas-Toussaint Charlet (French artist) 1792
Pieter de Hooch (Dutch painter) 1629
Claude Michel, "Clodian", (French sculptor) 1738
Robert Colquhoun (British artist) 1914

21
DECEMBER

Thomas Couture (French painter) 1815
Sir Thomas Graham Jackson (British architect) 1835
John Seymour Lucas (English painter) 1849
Tommaso di Giovanni, "Masaccio", (Italian painter) 1401

23
DECEMBER

John Marin (American painter) 1870
James McBey (British artist) 1883

22
DECEMBER

John Crome (English painter) 1768

24
DECEMBER

Gainsborough Dupont (English painter) 1754
Hans von Marees (German painter) 1837
Pierre Soulages (French painter) 1919

Girls on a Bridge EDVARD MUNCH (1863-1944)

25
DECEMBER

Jacob Houbraken (Dutch engraver) 1698
Yoshio Markino (Japanese artist) 1874
Sir William Nicholson (English artist) 1781
Maurice Utrillo (French painter) 1883

27
DECEMBER

Stanley William Hayter (English artist) 1901
Ernest William Tristram (Painter & Art Historian) 1882

26
DECEMBER

Alexandre-Marie Lenoir (French archaeologist & painter) 1761

28
DECEMBER

Philip Wilson Steer (English painter) 1860
Félix Edouard Vallotton (French artist) 1865

Grace
JEAN BAPTISTE
SIMEON CHARDIN
(1699-1779)

29
DECEMBER

Thomas Banks (English sculptor) 1735
Julius Cesar Ibbetson (English artist) 1759
Thomas Heaphy (English painter) 1775
Jean-Baptiste Joseph Pater (French painter) 1695

30
DECEMBER

Charles Catton (English painter) 1756
Henrietta Rae (English painter) 1859
Austin Osman Spare (British artist) 1886

31
DECEMBER

Aimé Jules Dalou (French sculptor) 1838
Cathleen Sabine Man (English painter) 1896
Charles Marshall (English painter) 1806
Henri Matisse (French painter) 1869

Les Demoiselles
d'Avignon (1907)
PABLO PICASSO
(1881-1973)

NOTES

NOTES

COVER
Paul Helleu Sketching with his Wife 1889
JOHN SINGER SARGENT (1856-1925)

FRONTISPIECE
Study for Two Apostles
RAPHAEL (1483-1520)

This daybook records the birthdays of painters, artists, sculptors and architects. The birthdays are either known or traditionally accepted dates. Notable but unavoidable omissions occur when no accurate record of birth could be found.

Painters, sculptors and architects are listed as such. The word artist has been used for painters who are recognized in more than one of the fine arts. MARJORIE GULLETT. 1989

The Publishers are very grateful to the following organisations, individuals and institutions for their kind permission to reproduce their pictures: The Ashmolean Museum, Oxford; The Bridgeman Art Library; The Brooklyn Museum, New York; Christie's Colour Library; Prado, Photographie Giraudon; Trustees of the Goodwood Estate; Mauritshuis, The Hague; Kunsthalle, Hamburg; Acquired through the Lillie P. Bliss Bequest, The Museum of Modern Art, New York; Musées Nationaux, France; The National Gallery, London; Scala; Musée St Denis, Rheims; The Tate Gallery, London.

PUBLISHED BY ALAN HUTCHISON PUBLISHING CO
9 PEMBRIDGE STUDIOS, 27A PEMBRIDGE VILLAS, LONDON W11 3EP

WORLDWIDE DISTRIBUTION

HELPING THE ENVIRONMENT

All the pages of this book are made from woodfree products (plant fibres, rags, grass etc). The cover boards contain low grade particles of renewable soft wood.

PRINTED AND BOUND IN HONG KONG

DESIGNED BY STEVE KIBBLE

ISBN 185272 9686